# The Complete Organist

## Book One

# The Complete Organist

## Book One

*One hundred pieces from across the centuries*

Kevin Mayhew

We hope you enjoy *The Complete Organist.*
Further copies are available from your local music shop
or Christian bookshop.

In case of difficulty, please contact the publisher direct by writing to:

The Sales Department
KEVIN MAYHEW LTD
Rattlesden
Bury St Edmunds
Suffolk IP30 0SZ

Phone 0449 737978
Fax 0449 737834

Please ask for our complete catalogue of outstanding Church Music.

First published in Great Britain in 1992 by Kevin Mayhew Ltd



ISBN 0 86209 324 4



Front Cover: Detail from "Venus and the Graces" by Sandro Botticelli (1445-1510).
Detached fresco, Louvre, Paris.
Photograph: © R. M. N. Reproduced by permission.

Cover design by Graham Johnstone
Picture Research: Jane Rayson
Printed and bound in Great Britain.

# Contents

# Foreword

*The Complete Organist* Book One is a collection of one hundred attractive and useful pieces. There is nothing here to cause a raised eyebrow in those possessing a moderate technique, but plenty to charm the ear. For the musician called upon to provide Service music week by week this book will come as a godsend, gathering under one cover, as it does, so many short pieces in such a variety of styles and moods.

In keeping with modern editorial practice the text of *The Complete Organist* is generally uncluttered with manual and registration suggestions. This approach enables the notes to speak for themselves and allows the performer to make his or her own choice in these matters. It also makes the actual process of reading the music easier.

We hope that many organists will gain much pleasure from these pieces: we have certainly enjoyed choosing them.

THE PUBLISHER

# PRELUDE on 'St Columba'

Charles Villiers Stanford (1852-1924)

3
3
Sw.
Gt.
Sw.

Gt.
Sw.
Gt.
Sw. mp
p
pp

# ANDANTE IN D

Felix Mendelssohn (1809-1847)

mf
rit.

# FANTASIA

Samuel Scheidt (1587-1654)

Gr
8' Fl

All
Sw Ob
f

p
CRESC
DIM
NEXT BAR!
f

# ADAGIO

Felix Mendelssohn (1809-1847)

rit.
pp a tempo

# ROMANCE

Gabriel Fauré (1845-1924) arr. Alan Ridout

mp

poco rit.
a tempo
p
3

pp

# REVERIE

Alexandre Boëly (1785-1858)

Gt.
Sw.
Gt.
Sw.
Gt.
Gt.

# PANIS ANGELICUS

César Franck (1822-1890) arr. Noel Rawsthorne

Sw.
mp
p
Gt.
mp
cresc.

cresc.
dim. poco a poco
Sw.
poco rall. e dim.
pp

# MENUET GOTHIQUE

Léon Boëllmann (1862-1897)

ff

p
ff
p

ff
p
ff
p

f
ff

# PIE JESU from 'Requiem'

Gabriel Fauré (1845-1924) arr. Noel Rawsthorne

Sw. p
Gt.
p
dolce
p
LH
RH

LH
RH
Sw.
pp
poco rall.
mp a tempo
p
Sw
pp
rall.

# I KNOW THAT MY REDEEMER LIVETH

George Frideric Handel (1685-1759) arr. Noel Rawsthorne

Sw.
mf
3
3
Gt. mf
mp
Sw.
Gt.

Sw.
Gt.

Sw.
mf
Gt. mf
mp

Sw.
3
Gt.
cresc.

ten.
Sw.
p
Gt.
rit.
a tempo
Sw.
mf
3
poco rit.

# RHAPSODY

Camille Saint-Saëns (1835-1921)

Gt.
L.H.
Sw.
pp
Gt.
cresc.
p
Gt.

Sw.
pp
poco rit.
ppp

# FUGUE

Felix Mendelssohn (1809-1847)

cresc.
poco a poco

ff
rit.

# COMMUNION

Camille Saint-Saëns (1835-1921)

cresc.
dim.
p
L.H.

pp
R.H.
f
L.H.
pp
ff
mf
L.H.

p
sim.
mf
dim.
pp

pp
quasi recitativo
3
p
pp
pp
dim.
ppp

# AIR

Alexandre Boëly (1785-1858)

# RÊVERIE

Noel Rawsthorne (b. 1929)

cresc.
mf
dim.
ten.
p
poco a poco rall. al fine
dim.
pp

# ANDANTE IN B♭

Felix Mendelssohn (1809-1847)

ppp

# PRELUDE IN G

Gustav Merkel (1827-1885)

# ELEGY

Malcolm Archer (b. 1952)

Gt.
mf
add
f

+ Sw. reeds
allarg.
ff
a tempo
Tempo primo
rall.
reduce
Sw. p
pp
poco rit.
Gt. 8′ flute (or soft reed)
Gt. p
Sw.
rall.
pp

# JESU, JOY OF MAN'S DESIRING

Johann Sebastian Bach (1685-1750) arr. Noel Rawsthorne

Sw.
Gt.
Sw.
L.H.
Gt.

Sw.
Gt.
Sw.

Gt.
Sw.
Gt.
Sw.
Gt.

poco rit.
a tempo
Sw.
poco rit.

# ARRIVAL OF THE QUEEN OF SHEBA

George Frideric Handel (1685-1759) arr. Noel Rawsthorne

Sw.
p

Gt.
mf
Sw.
Sw.
p
Gt.
f

Sw.
p
Gt.
f
L.H.
Sw.
mf
Sw.
Gt.

Sw.
Gt.
f
Sw.
mp

Gt.
mf
Sw.
Gt.

poco rall.

# CHORAL PRELUDE on 'Humility'

Malcolm Archer (b. 1952)

# GAVOTTE

William Boyce (1710-1779) arr. Noel Rawsthorne

Sw.
Gt.

Sw.
Gt.
poco rall.

# MELODY

Alexandre Guilmant (1837-1911)

rall.
a tempo

rit.
a tempo
rall.
ppp
a tempo

cresc.
dim. e rit.
rall.
ppp

# ANDANTE

Louis Lefébure-Wély (1817-1869)

Gt.
3
Sw.
rit.

a tempo

# PRELUDE

Alexandre Boëly (1785-1858)

tr
1.
2.

# COMMUNION IN E♭

Alexandre Guilmant (1837-1911)

p
Gt.
Sw.

cresc.
Gt.
Gt.
Sw.
L.H.
Sw.

Gt.
dim.
Sw.
pp
rit.
ppp

# CANTIQUE

Edward Elgar (1857-1934)

Gt. p
Sw. mf
cresc.
p
Gt. mf
f
Sw. p

cresc.
Gt. f
cresc.
dim.
Sw. p
pp
sostenuto
poco
cresc.

dim.
pp
ppp
poco rit.
tempo I cresc.
Gt. p
Sw. p

cresc.
cresc.
Gt. f
cresc.
allargando
ff

# GYMNOPÉDIE I

Erik Satie (1866-1925) arr. Alan Ridout

pp

# CLOISTER-GARTH

Herbert Brewer (1865-1928)

mp
pp
rit.
a tempo
Gt. mp

Sw.
p
lento
rall.

# CHRIST, THOU LAMB OF GOD

Johann Sebastian Bach (1685-1750)

# PRELUDE IN D MINOR

Alexandre Boëly (1785-1858)

# AIR from 'Suite No. 3 in D'

Johann Sebastian Bach (1685-1750) arr. Noel Rawsthorne

tr
tr
1.
2.
tr
tr
poco ritard.

# ANGELS FAREWELL from 'Dream of Gerontius'

Edward Elgar (1857-1934)

Gt.
poco rit.
a tempo
Sw.
Sw.

poco più mosso
Gt.
Sw.

Tempo I
pp
Gt.
mf
p
Sw.
Gt.

Sw.
Gt.
p
p
mp
pp
8va
poco a poco
rallentando
a tempo
p
p

mf
diminuendo
pp
pp
p Gt.
L.H.
R.H.
Sw.
mf
ppp

# LAMENT

Philip Moore (b. 1943)

Sw.
Gt.
mf
mf

Gt.
un poco rall. e dim.
Gt.
p a tempo
Sw.
un poco rall.

# PAVANE

Maurice Ravel (1875-1937) arr. Alan Ridout

# COMMUNION IN G

Alexandre Guilmant (1837-1911)

Gt.

Sw.
cresc.
dim.
Gt.
Gt.

cresc.
Sw. p
rall.
pp

# PRELUDE IN A MINOR

Gustav Merkel (1827-1885)

cresc.
mp
rit.
dim.
p

# ROMANCE

Edward MacDowell (1860-1908)

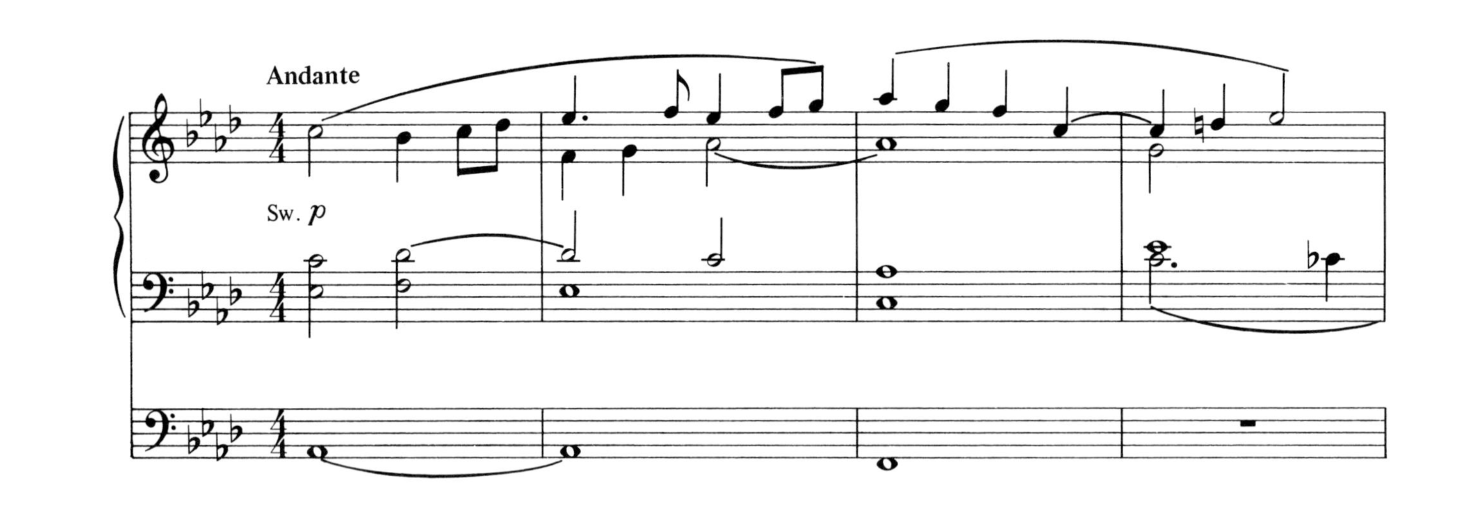

# BEHOLD, A ROSE IS BLOOMING

Johannes Brahms (1833-1897)

# CHRISTMAS PASTORALE

Jaak Nikolaas Lemmens (1823-1881)

L.H.

tr
tr
rall.

# WINTER from 'The Four Seasons'

Antonio Vivaldi (1678-1741) arr. Alan Ridout

# EVENING PRAYER

Henry Smart (1818-1879)

Gt. mf
Gt.

Sw.
Gt.
Gt.
Sw.
Gt.
Gt.

Sw. p
Sw. p
(+ Oboe)

(- Oboe)
Gt.

Sw.
poco rit.

# CHORAL PRELUDE on 'Melcombe'

C. Hubert H. Parry (1848-1918)

Sw.
Gt.
Sw.
Gt.
rit.

( ♩ = ♩. )
pp
Slower ( ♩. = ♩ )
dim.
rit.

# PLACIDAMENTE

Edward Hopkins (1818-1901)

Gt.
Sw.
Gt.
Sw.
Gt.

Sw.
dim. e rall.
pp

# TRUMPET TUNE

Christopher Tambling (b. 1964)

Gt.

Trumpet
Gt.
Trumpet

tr
Gt.
Trumpet

tr
Gt.
Trumpet
Gt.
Trumpet

Christ's Hospital, September 1981

# SHEEP MAY SAFELY GRAZE

Johann Sebastian Bach (1685-1750) arr. Noel Rawsthorne

Solo Flutes
Sw.
R.H.
Sw.
L.H. Sw.
Solo Flutes

Sw.
Solo Flutes

Sw.

poco rit.
a tempo
tr
Solo Flutes
Sw.

R.H. Sw.
Solo Flutes
L.H. Sw.
poco rall.

# TRIO IN G MINOR

Josef Rheinberger (1839-1901)

tr
rit.

# CHORAL PRELUDE IN G MINOR

Sigfrid Karg-Elert (1877-1933)

p
mp
p
Largo
pp

# POSTLUDE on 'Jesus Christ is Risen Today'

Noel Rawsthorne (b. 1929)

poco a poco allargando al Fine
Lento

# PASTORAL

Gustav Merkel (1827-1885)

pp
p

pp
dim.

# ROYAL KNIGHTS: A CEREMONIAL MARCH

Christopher Tambling (b. 1964)

cresc.
poco allargando
Sw.
Gt. cresc.
a tempo
Sw. Full mf
simile
mp
cresc.

mf
simile
Gt.
Sw.
Gt.
Sw.
Gt.
poco allargando
cresc.
Sw.
Gt. f
a tempo

cresc.
poco allargando
Gt.
Sw.
cresc.

# O WORLD, I NOW MUST LEAVE THEE

Johannes Brahms (1833-1897)

p
f
p
f

p
f
p
rit.

# ANDANTE from 'The Death of Ase'

Edvard Grieg (1843-1907) arr. Alan Ridout

f
ff
mp

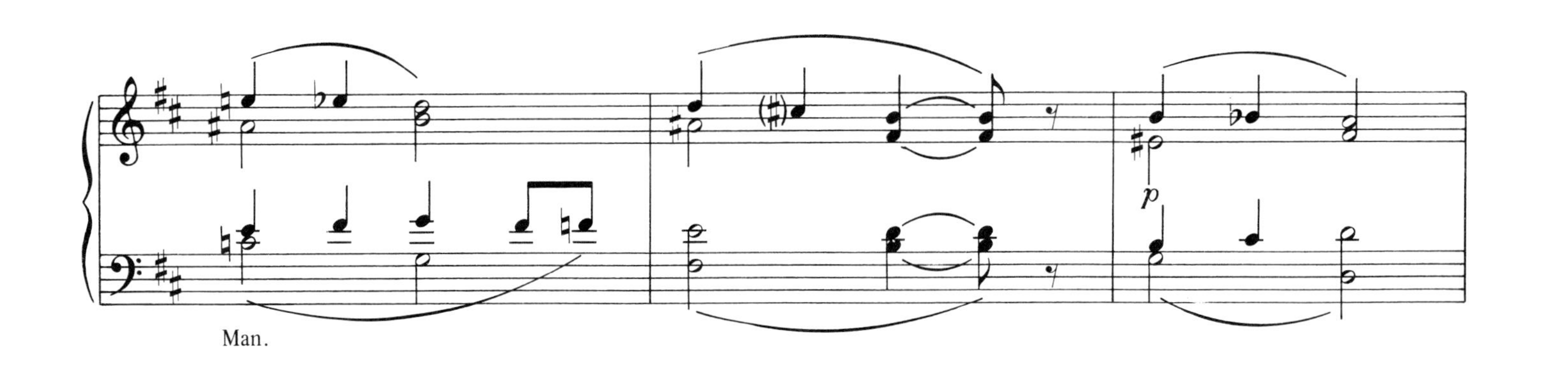

p
Man.


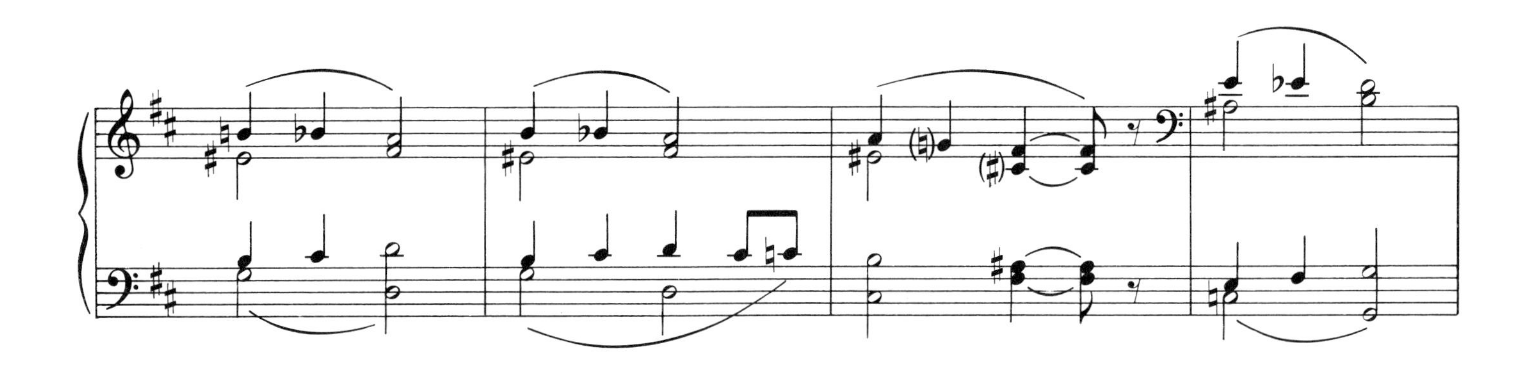

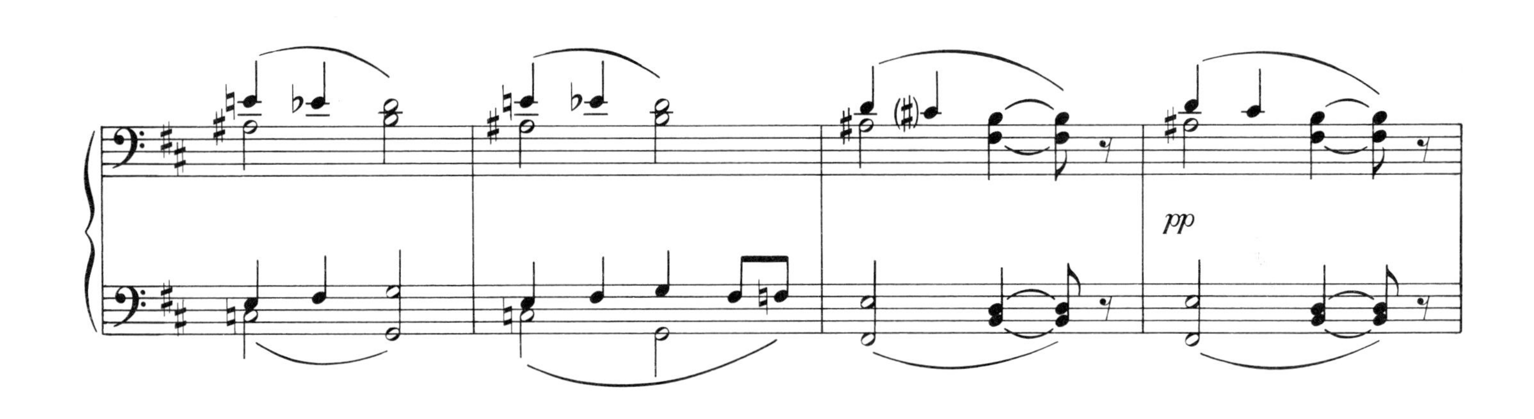

pp

# SUMMER from 'The Four Seasons'

Antonio Vivaldi (1678-1741) arr. Alan Ridout

Presto
f stacc.
Adagio
p
Presto
f stacc.
Adagio
p

# CHORAL PRELUDE IN G

Sigfrid Karg-Elert (1877-1933)

Sw.
p
Gt.
Sw.
p
Gt.
allargando

# KOMM, SÜSSER TOD (Come Sweet Death)

Johann Sebastian Bach (1685-1750) arr. Noel Rawsthrone

Sw.
p
poco rall.

# GLORIA

François Couperin (1668-1733)

# PETITE PIECE

Alexandre Boëly (1785-1858)

Gt.
Sw.
Sw.
Gt.
Gt.
Sw.
Gt.
Sw.

Gt.
Sw.
Sw.

# TE DEUM PRELUDE

Marc-Antoine Charpentier (1634-1704) arr. Noel Rawsthorne

Tutti
Solo

Tutti
Solo
poco rall.

# TRUMPET VOLUNTARY

Jeremiah Clarke (1670-1707) arr. Noel Rawsthorne

Solo Trumpet
f
Sw.
Gt.
ff
+ Gt. to Ped.
Solo Trumpet
f
Sw.
– Gt. to Ped.

f
simile
Gt.
ff
+ Gt. to Ped.

Solo Trumpet
f
Sw.
– Gt. to Ped.
Gt.
ff
+ Gt. to Ped.
ff broader
poco rall.

# PRELUDE IN G

Charles Villiers Stanford (1852-1924)

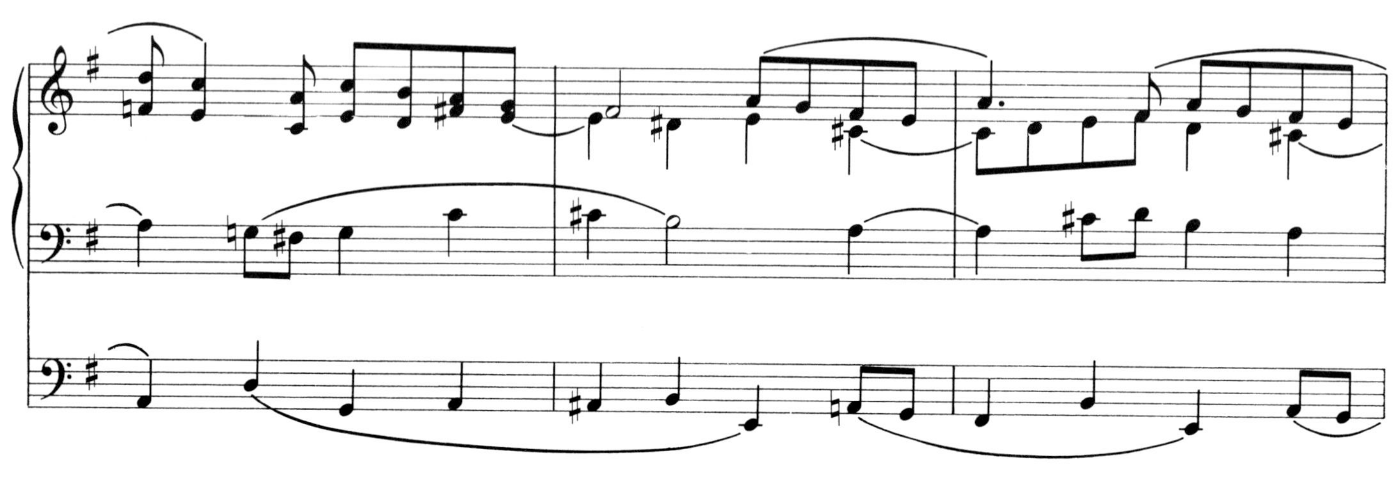

Gt. (Clarinet)
p
Sw.
p
pp

# BELOVED JESUS

Johannes Brahms (1833-1897)

p
f

# INTERMEZZO

Max Reger (1873-1916)

mf
pp
p
pp
p
pp
poco rit.
a tempo
p
p
mf
p
pp L.H.

L.H.
L.H.
f
p
p
pp

# MARCH

John Marsh (b. 1939)

Full Sw.
mf
Gt. to Ped. off
Sw. Ped.
L.H.
3
cresc.
rall.
a tempo
Gt. ff
f
Gt. to Ped.

legato
Sw. mp

Gt. mf
Sw.
Tempo primo
Gt. ff

molto rall.
marcato
Slow

# REFLECTION

Alexandre Boëly (1785-1858)

tr

# O FOR THE WINGS OF A DOVE

Felix Mendelssohn (1809-1847) arr. Alan Ridout

# CHORAL IMPROVISATION IN G

Sigfrid Karg-Elert (1877-1933)

Gt. p
Solo (Clarinet)
sonoro, ma delicato

# FOLK TUNE on 'Dream Angus'

Christopher Tambling (b. 1964)

Gt. Flutes 8 + 4
Sw. Diaps. + Oboe 8

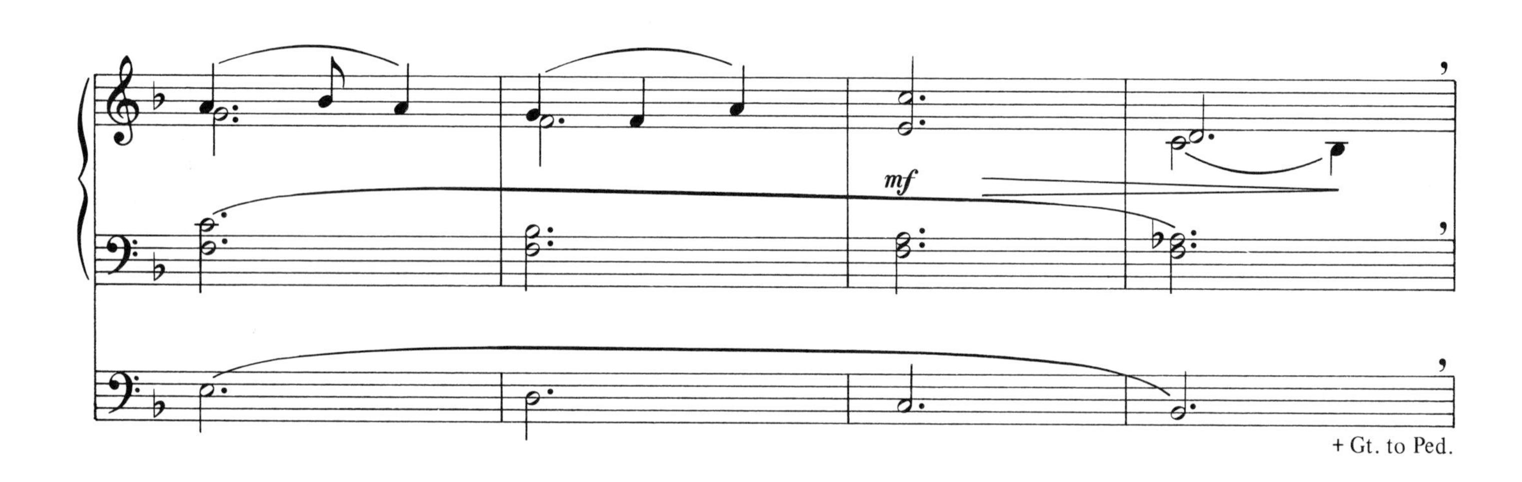

mf
mf
mp
poco più mosso
Gt. + Diap 8

cresc.
f
Gt. + Principal 4
poco rit.
Tempo I
Gt. – Principal 4
mf
Sw.
– Gt. to Ped.

cresc.
mf
dim.
meno mosso
rit.
mp
rit.
p

# BIST DU BEI MIR

Johann Sebastian Bach (1685-1750) arr. Noel Rawsthorne

tr
poco rall.

# SOLILOQUY

Gustav Merkel (1827-1885)

# PRELUDE IN F

Charles Villiers Stanford (1852-1924)

mf

p
pp

# INVOCATION

Ernest Bryson (1867-1942)

Gt. mf
cresc.

Sw. p
f
poco rall.
a tempo
poco staccato
Gt.

Gt.
mf
cresc.
mf
Sw. p
L.H.
pp
rall.

# PRELUDE

Michael Gotthardt Fischer (1775-1829)

# ADAGIETTO from 'Symphony V'

Gustav Mahler (1860-1911) arr. Noel Rawsthorne

ten.
Sw. pp
Gt. p
espress.
Gt.
ten.
Sw.
pp
poco a poco cresc.
f
Gt.
Sw.

ten.
p espressivo
pp
p molto espress.
pp
Sw.
Gt. p
morendo
Sw.

Gt. pp
ppp
poco a poco cresc.
8ve
f
Gt.
loco
dim.
ppp

# GYMNOPÉDIE III

Erik Satie (1866-1925) arr. Alan Ridout

pp

# NOW THANK WE ALL OUR GOD

Sigfrid Karg-Elert (1877-1933)

Gt.
fff
12
fff
tr

Sw.
mf
tr
più gravemente
p
pp

ff Gt.
9
fff
tr
R.H.
R.H.
L.H.
L.H.
tr

Sw.
f
fff
Gt.
12

fff
tr
rall.

# BERCEUSE

Louis Vierne (1870-1937)

Gt.
Sw.
Gt.
Sw.
Gt. mf

dim.
Sw. pp

pp
cresc.
dim. e rit. poco a poco

# BLESSED ARE YE, FAITHFUL SOULS

Johannes Brahms (1833-1897)

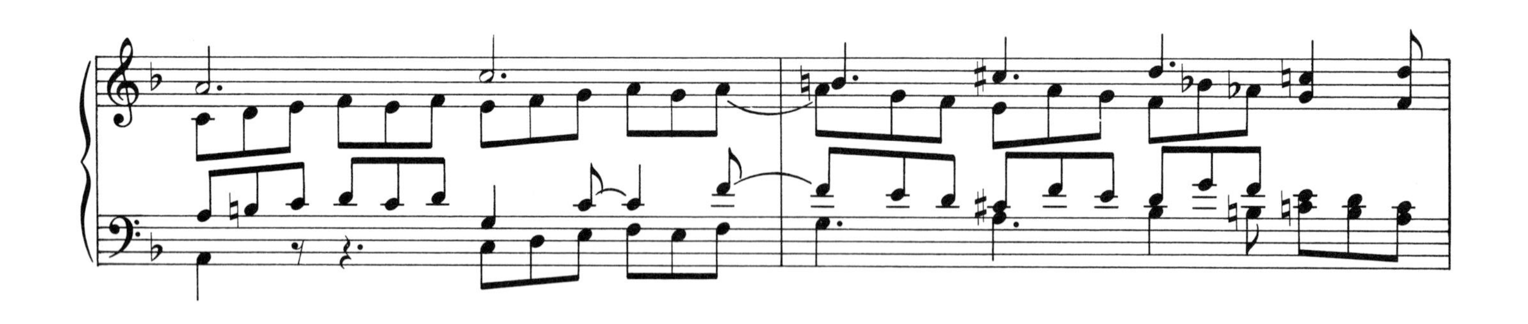

# PROCESSIONAL

Anthony Milner (b. 1925)

f

mf
mf

poco rall.
p

# MEMORIES AND REGRETS

Colin Mawby (b. 1936)

f
mf
p
pp
Gt. Solo
mf
Sw. p
Sw. p
dim.
pp

# ANDANTE

Felix Mendelssohn (1809-1847)

Sw.
Gt.

Sw.
L.H.
Gt.
Sw.
Gt.
Sw.

# NIMROD

Edward Elgar (1857-1934) arr. Alan Ridout

(♭)
pp
p
cresc.
p

f
3
3
ff
mf
p

# O REST IN THE LORD from 'Elijah'

Felix Mendelssohn (1809-1847) arr. Noel Rawsthorne

Tempo I
p
pp
poco rit.
cresc.
dim.
cresc.
dim.
p
pp
dim.
Sw. pp
pp
poco rall.

# GRAZIOSO

Henry Smart (1818-1879)

Sw. (+ reed)
Gt.

Gt. (clarinet)
Sw. (– reed)

Sw.
poco rit.
a tempo

poco rit.

# THE ENCHANTED GARDEN

Maurice Ravel (1875-1937) arr. Alan Ridout

pp
mf
p
pp
cresc.
f
dim.

rit.
pp a tempo
p cresc.
mp cresc.
mf cresc.
ff

# CHORAL IMPROVISATION IN A

Sigfrid Karg-Elert (1877-1933)

Sw. mf
p
Gt. f
Sw. p
pp allargando
Gt. a tempo
f
meno f
Sw. p
pp
p
pp
poco a poco allargando e pesante
p
pp allargando
Gt. f cresc.
fff

# LARGO from 'Concerto in D Minor'

Antonio Vivaldi (1678-1741) arr. Noel Rawsthorne

Sw.
poco rall.

# INTERLUDE

Alexandre Boëly (1785-1858)

Gt.
Sw.

Gt.

# SOLEMN MELODY

Walford Davies (1869-1941) arr. Noel Rawsthorne

Gt. mf
Sw. mp
cresc.
mp
p
p
pp
(+ Full Sw.)
poco rall.
Gt.
f
ff

Sw. f
Gt.
ff
fff
dim. poco a poco al fine
3
3
mf
Sw. mp
rall.
p
Gt.
pp

# ANDANTE TRANQUILLO

Peter Warlock (1894-1930) arr. Noel Rawsthorne

Sw.
Solo
mp
Sw.
1.
2.
Meno mosso
Sw.
p
rall.

# LENTO

Louis Marchand (1669-1732)

# ELEVATION

Alexandre Guilmant (1837-1911)

Sw. cresc.
f
p

Gt.
Sw.
cresc.
f
dim.
p
pp

# PRELUDE IN F

Alexandre Boëly (1785-1858)

# ARIA

Noel Rawsthorne (b. 1929)

Sw. mp
cresc. poco a poco
dim. poco a poco
poco rall.
ten.
ten.

Gt. mp
sempre legato
Sw. p
quasi pizzicato
poco rall.

# VERSET IN THE FORM OF A CANON

Samuel Alexandre Rousseau (1853-1904)

# LARGO

Michel Corrette (1709-1795)

Gr
Sw
Gr

# IDYLL

Edward MacDowell (1860-1908)

Gt.
Sw.
pp
p
Sw.
pp
Gt.
Sw. pp

# SARABANDE

Edvard Grieg (1843-1907) arr. Alan Ridout

pp
cresc.
mf

# AUTUMN from 'The Four Seasons'

Antonio Vivaldi (1678-1741) arr. Alan Ridout

f

# LARGO

George Frideric Handel (1685-1759) arr. Noel Rawsthorne

3

mf
poco allargando
3
a tempo
Sw.
mf
poco rall.
pp